THE STORY OF
Robert
BRUCE

KT-430-273

CORBIE

Text by David Ross
Illustrated by Susan Hutchison

© 1998 Waverley Books Ltd
Reprinted 1999, 2000, 2002, 2003, 2004, 2006

Published by Waverley Books Ltd,
New Lanark, Scotland

ISBN 10: 1 902407 03 2
ISBN 13: 978 1 902407 03 6

Printed and bound in UAE

THE STORY OF
ROBERT BRUCE

I, Robert the First, by God's grace king of Scots, send you greetings! My message comes from far away in time, for I lived more than six hundred years before you were born. I know nothing about you or the times you live in. No doubt they are much changed since my own days, but I hope that my kingdom of Scotland still plays a part in the affairs of the world, as I tried to make it do.

My story is not just the story of Robert Bruce. Many people helped me. I had brave friends, and many of them died to help me become king. I also had fierce enemies. I myself did many bad things, including one terrible thing. I shall tell you about them. It is right that you children of a future age should know what the men of old times did to maintain their freedom and the freedom of Scotland.

Where shall I start? When I was a child, perhaps. I was a lucky child, for I was born into the great family of Bruce. My father was a lord, and his father was a lord. We had lands both in Scotland and in England. Every year my father went to England and spent time on his estates there, but our real home was in Scotland, in Carrick, near the sea.

Most children in my young days were put to work as soon as they were about seven years old. They spent their days toiling in the fields, chopping wood or carrying coal, helping in whatever work their fathers did. But I was the eldest son of the great Earl of Carrick. We lived in the upper rooms of a strong castle. I did not have to work, except at my lessons. I had to learn to speak and write in three languages, French, Latin and Scots. There was another language, too, which my nurse spoke and so did all the country people around. That was the Gaelic language. When I was still a tiny boy, I learned to speak Gaelic, and in my adventures to come I was heartily glad that I did because it was the Gaelic-speaking people of the Western Isles who looked after me during the

worst days of my life. But I liked better to learn how to ride and how to fight. I had many brothers and sisters and used to lead them all as if they were my army. My grandfather used to laugh to see us. But once he picked me up in his arms and said, "Perhaps one day you will lead an army. Never forget that you are descended from the old Scottish kings. The destiny of the Bruces lies in Scotland. By rights we should be its kings."

As I grew older, I discovered that my grandfather had actually tried to become the king of Scotland, but another man, also a descendant of the old kings, had been chosen instead. His name was King John.

When I was a young man I did not care much about all that. When my old grandfather died, my father became Lord of Annandale and I became the Earl of Carrick. I admit now that I cared more about keeping my earldom in Scotland and my lands in England than I did about the freedom of Scotland.

And the freedom of Scotland was in deadly danger. That great nation to the south, England, had a strong and fearless king, Edward the First. I was presented to him at his court in London when I was a very young man. He was kind and friendly

to me, although he was a man who could make other men cry. Edward did not want Scotland to be a free and independent country. He wanted it to be under his control. When he did not like what King John of Scotland was doing, he sent an army and captured John. John's crown was taken away, and he was brought to London and put in prison. Now Scotland had no king, and Edward sent governors from England to rule the country in his own name.

At this time a man called William Wallace appeared. Like me, he was young. Unlike me, he was not one of the great lords of the country. He owned no land. No men were under his command. He was the younger son of a country squire, but it was he who raised an army and in a great battle defeated the English army at the bridge of Stirling. Excited by what Wallace had done and seeing that nearly all the people in Scotland supported him, I called out my own men of Carrick and I too set out to fight for King John of Scotland.

I was not much of a leader in those days. When an English army appeared to fight us, my men ran away and I could not stop them. Soon after that I once again promised my loyalty to King Edward and did no more to help Wallace. At last he was captured, brought to London and cruelly put to death. Once again Edward was master of all Scotland.

I had never forgotten what my grandfather had said. Now I thought, being a proud young man, that I would break my promise of loyalty to Edward and fight to bring a king to the throne of Scotland again. Not John, who had lost his crown, but myself!

I did not know what a harsh and difficult task it would be. There were men whose help I would need. The most important of these was John Comyn, whose family estates were even greater than those of the Bruces. He too was a man with a claim to be king, although not as good a claim as mine. We had never been friends, but I made him a tempting offer. If he helped me to become king, I would give him the Bruce lands of Carrick and Annandale. After me, he would be the greatest man in the kingdom.

We met in the Greyfriars church in Dumfries. We had both promised safety to each other, but the meeting went dreadfully wrong. Comyn would have nothing to do with my offer. He would never allow a Bruce to be the greatest man in the kingdom. In my anger I struck him with my dagger, and he fell dying in front of the altar. It was a most wicked deed. When they heard what I had done, many people who would have helped me refused. But there was no going back now, and my closest friends did not desert me. One of these was good Robert Wishart, the bishop of Glasgow. Another was William Lamberton, bishop of St Andrews. Even though I had committed a mortal sin, they stayed by me. But, most of all, I was glad to have with me Sir James Douglas, a great warrior and faithful friend.

A few weeks later we went to the ancient abbey of Scone where for centuries the kings of Scotland

had been crowned. The Coronation Stone had been taken away to London by Edward for his own royal abbey of Westminster. The ancient family of Macduff had always been the ones to crown the king, but Macduff, the Earl of Fife, was just a boy and in King

Edward's power. His sister, Isabel, Countess of Buchan, with great bravery came to crown me king of Scotland.

I was a king now, but I was far from being the master of my kingdom. I had hoped that the Scottish lords would support me, but most did not. Many of them were relations of John Comyn, whom I had murdered, and the man who considered himself Scotland's overlord, Edward of England, was determined to crush me. His anger was all the greater because I had once promised to be his faithful servant. Now I was claiming to be his equal, an independent king who owed loyalty to no one. His people mockingly called me "King Hob".

This was the time when everything began to go wrong. First of all I was beaten in a battle, at Methven, near Perth. After that I no longer had an army. I had to hide in the Highland mountains, and even there I was hunted by the friends of Comyn. Then Elizabeth, my queen, was captured at Tain by the Earl of Ross along with my daughter Marjorie, my sister Mary and other women of my family. Ross handed them over to King Edward, who treated them shamefully, especially my sister Mary and Isabel of Buchan. He had them

imprisoned in cages, like animals, for his people to jeer at. When any of the men who supported me were caught, they were put to death. For me, no place was safe for long. I had to leave Scotland in a small boat and sail to the island of Rathlin, off the coast of Ireland.

For months I roamed among the islands, helped by many people, with enemies often close behind. Sometimes I slept out on the open hillside, sometimes in caves. Only a short time ago, I heard a strange story about this time of my life. It was told that I was hiding all alone in a cave, sad and lonely, and wondering if it was not best to give up the struggle to be a proper king. Then I saw a spider swinging on its thread from the low roof of the cave and trying to reach the wall.

Each time it tried it never quite got there, but it did not give up. It kept on swinging to and fro until at last it did reach the wall, and it clung there. "I will be like the

spider," said the Bruce of this story. "I too will keep on trying and never give up."

I laughed when I heard the tale. Although I had slept in many caves, I had never seen a spider. But the spirit of the story was true. At that time I almost did give up. Then I thought of all the people who had died for my sake, of my sister shut up in a cage, of my proud country under the harsh rule of Edward. I knew I could not give up. I sailed back to the mainland to start again.

Seven long years followed, years of fighting and hardship. King Edward tried to find me with a great army. With only a small band of followers I recaptured some of the castles taken by Edward, but I knew that I was not ready to fight a great battle. My men were far hardier now than when I first set out to fight with William Wallace, and I had learned how to lead them in war. We won two small but fierce battles, and after that more and more men were ready to join us. Most of the castles in Scotland were held by Edward's men. One by one we stormed them, usually at night. I remember how astonished a French knight was to see that it was I who led my men through the icy waters of the moat at Perth, over the walls and into the town. But it was because I shared their

dangers that the men of Scotland were willing to fight for me as their king. I was a changed man from the proud and fiery young nobleman who let his army run away at Irvine.

Old King Edward of England died, but his son, Edward the Second, kept up the war. By this time I had won back nearly all of Scotland without fighting any large battle. In such a fight, I thought, the power of the heavily armed English knights and the terrifying accuracy of the English archers would inevitably mean defeat. By then very few castles were still in English hands, but one that was, the strong fortress of Stirling, was bravely held. My brother Edward made a foolish agreement with its commander. If no English army came to relieve him within a year, he would surrender the castle to me. So at last came the great challenge. Edward the Second was not the man his father was, but there was no doubt that he would come to save Stirling for otherwise he would be shamed in front of every king in Europe. He would come with enough strength to crush Robert Bruce's kingship for ever. I had a year to prepare for this. How quickly it passed!

By the agreement, King Edward had to be within three miles of Stirling by 24th June. The year was

1314. He arrived on the 23rd with a great army of foot-soldiers but also with many mounted knights in armour. I feared these more than the foot-soldiers for we had very few such knights. My host of men came from all over Scotland, from the far Highlands in the north to the far-off hills of Galloway in the south. Some even came from the king of Norway's islands of Orkney, but King Edward's army was far larger.

At least we could prepare the ground. I made my men dig pits in the earth and cover them with brushwood sticks and grass in the hope that the English heavy horses would fall in.

The battle lasted two warm, sunny days. Before the fighting really started, something happened that made my two chief commanders, Sir James Douglas and Randolph, Earl of Moray, angry with me.

"If you are killed then we are lost," they said. What happened was this. A band of English knights, riding ahead of their main army, came suddenly out of the trees and saw us. I was riding out in front of the army, not on my tall war-horse but on a little light saddle horse. An English knight, Sir Henry de Bohun, saw the gold circle round my helmet and realised I was the Bruce. He rode at me with his lance full tilt. I saw him coming and, just in time, pulled my little horse aside. Then as he galloped past me, I rose in my stirrups and gave him a great stroke with my battle-axe so that it broke. Sir Henry lay dead on the ground. My Scotsmen gave a great shout of triumph. To Douglas and Moray, I said I was only sorry that I had broken my good battle-axe.

Later that day there was hard fighting when another group of heavily armoured knights tried to make their way round us and get to Stirling. The Earl of Moray was placed to stop this, but he was almost too late. I had to give him a sharp

reminder. But his soldiers, with their spears and shields placed together in the square-shaped groups that we called schiltroms, forced back the supposedly unbeatable knights. By then it was late. The day ended well for me and my Scots, but the battle was not yet won. I was far from sure that we would win it, and I almost ordered my army to retreat into the hills and wait for the English to go home. But a Scots knight, one of those who still fought for the English king, came in the short midsummer dark to my camp. He told me that the English army had lost heart and, for all their numbers, could be beaten. I asked my commanders what they thought.

"Good king," they said, "as soon as day comes tomorrow, order yourself and your army for battle. We shall not fail for fear of death nor flinch at any suffering till we have made our country free."

So it was decided. At daybreak I gave the order, and my brother Edward led forward his men to open the attack. But then they stopped, and knelt down, and said the Lord's Prayer. After the battle I was told that King Edward saw them and said, "See, they pray for mercy."

"Yes, but from God, not from you," said one of his knights.

It was not an easy victory. Hardest for me was to watch without fighting. One more sword or axe would make no difference, and my task was to make certain my army followed my plan. Under my own cousin, the Earl of Gloucester, the English cavalry levelled their lances and charged at us. Who would have thought that men without armour, apart from their shields, could have resisted them? But my three schiltroms held steady. Gloucester was killed, and my spearmen pressed in on the Englishmen. At last the English massed their archers to one side and began to rain arrows into our formations. This was what I had feared most. I had no heavy cavalry like Edward of England's, but I had some horsemen, lightly armoured, under the trusty Marischal of Scotland, Sir Robert Keith. At my signal, Keith led his riders down on to the archers and swept them away in a furious charge.

The centre of the battle was a heaving mass of men, with the mailed knights rising above them and sometimes toppling and falling. I had a whole brigade of Highlanders under my own command, and I had made them wait until I saw where they would most be needed. Now, at last, I let them go, aiming for the right, where the English seemed strongest, and they raced into the battle shouting their wild Gaelic war-cries. Now my whole army was in the thick of battle. Across all the front of their battle line, the English found themselves being forced back. At last they broke, and my men

were no longer fighting them but chasing them. Many fell into the Bannock Burn and were drowned, many more were slain. King Edward, who they say had fought bravely, fled from the field, and although Sir James Douglas pursued him, he got safely away.

I had never intended to fight such a battle, but we had won it. To my countrymen, and to me, it seemed that our prayers had indeed been answered. It was still many years before England could bring herself to accept that Scotland, as a free land, had her own king. During that time, and since, I tried to rule justly and fairly and to be a king worthy of the sacrifices that my people had made. How well I have succeeded I cannot tell.

But this much I do know – my country is at peace, is free and lives under the law. And I have a young son, David, to follow as king when I am gone.

And I am ill and weary now. I had hoped once that I would lead an army of Scots in a holy war, joining the great fight to chase the Saracens from Spain. I know that cannot be, but I have ordered that when I am dead the heart shall be taken from my body, placed in a casket and brought on crusade by worthy knights of Scotland. In this way I shall fulfil the dearest wish of my living heart and show that my kingdom too can play a part in the great affairs of the world.

SOME DATES FROM THE LIFE OF
ROBERT I, KING OF SCOTS

- Born 1274

- Battle of Irvine, July 1297

- Battle of Stirling Bridge, September 1297

- Execution of Wallace, August 1305

- Murder of John Comyn, February 1306

- Coronation, March 25th, 1306

- Battle of Methven, June 1306

- Escape to Rathlin, September 1306

- Return to Carrick, February 1307

- Truce given to Stirling Castle, June 1313

- Capture of Edinburgh Castle, March 1314

- Battle of Bannockburn, 23rd-24th June 1314

- The pope acknowledges Bruce as King of Scots, January 1324

- England acknowledges Bruce as King of Scots, 4th May 1328

- Death, 7th June 1329